Disney · PIXAR

THE WORLD OF Cars

ANNUAL 2009

EGMONT
We bring stories to life

First published in Great Britain in 2008
by Egmont UK Limited
239 Kensington High Street, London W8 6SA
© Disney Enterprises, Inc. and Pixar

Editor: Jaine Keskeys
Art Editor: Phil Williams

Disney/Pixar elements ©Disney/Pixar; Dodge®; Hudson Hornet™; ©Volkswagen AG; Hummer®; Model T™;
Fiat™; Mack®; Mazda Miata®; Kenworth®; Peterbilt®; Porsche®; Jeep®; Mercury™; Plymouth Superbird™;
Cadillac Coupe de Ville®; Ferrari®; Fairlane™; Petty® Chevrolet Impala™; Sarge's rank insignia design used with
the approval of the U.S. Army; Inspired by the Cadillac Ranch by Ant Farm (Lord, Michels and Marquez) © 1974.

Note to parents: adult supervision is recommended when sharp-pointed items, such as scissors, are in use.

ISBN 978 1 4052 3903 5
1 3 5 7 9 10 8 6 4 2
Printed in Italy

All rights reserved. No part of this publication may be reproduced, stored in a retrieval system, or transmitted, in any form or by any means,
electronic, mechanical, photocopying, recording or otherwise, without the prior permission of the publisher and copyright owner.

This annual belongs to

Name

Age

My favourite character is

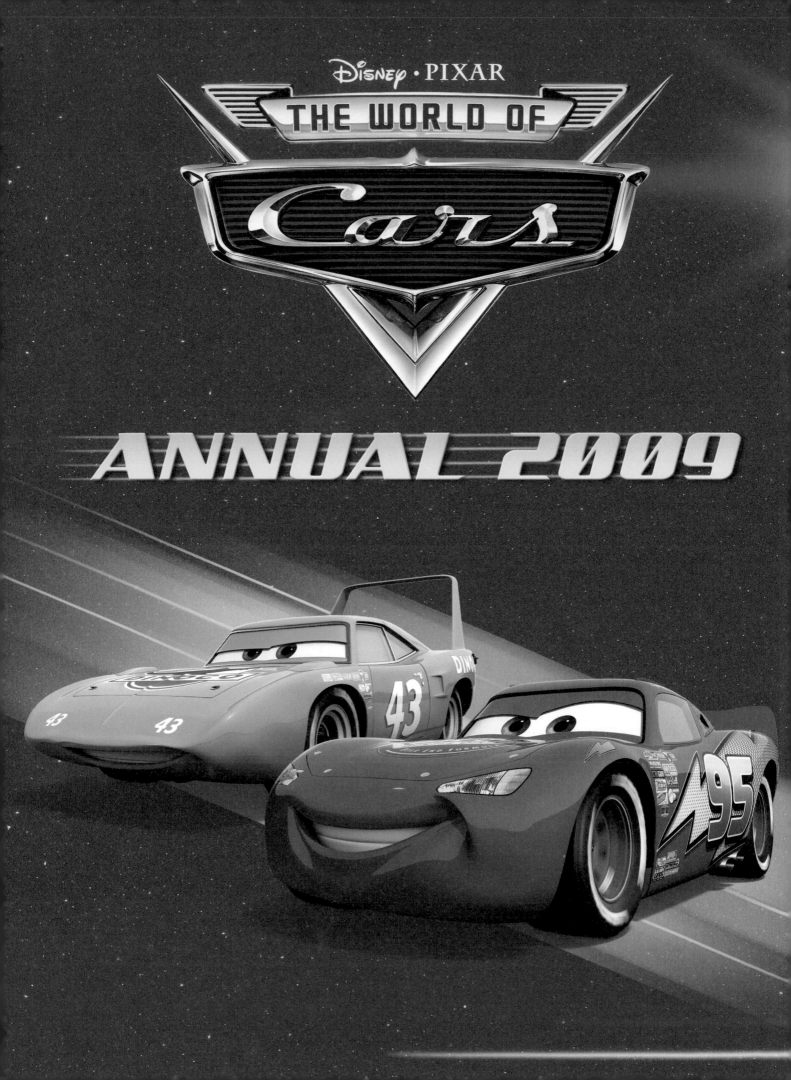

Lightning McQueen

McQueen is a rookie race car, hoping to win both the Piston Cup and Dinoco sponsorship. But the final race of the season finishes in a three-way tie between McQueen, The King and Chick Hicks. On his way to the decider race, McQueen gets lost in Radiator Springs, where he makes some new friends who teach him there's more to life than winning races.

Mack

Mack, a Super-Liner truck, pulls McQueen's trailer to his races. During the long drive to the decider race, Mack falls asleep and accidentally dumps a sleeping McQueen on to the road. When Mack wakes up, he is unaware that McQueen is lost in Radiator Springs!

The King

The King, sponsored by Dinoco, is a veteran race car who ties with McQueen and Chick Hicks in the final race. He's already won nine Piston Cups and tells McQueen that he'd be nowhere without his team. But McQueen only thinks about taking over the Dinoco sponsorship when The King retires!

Chick Hicks

Chick Hicks has spent his career coming in second to The King and is quite bitter about this. Determined to do whatever it takes to win, Chick often cheats, by ramming other cars and causing crashes on the track.

Tex Dinoco

Tex is the owner of Dinoco, the company that sponsors The King. McQueen wants to win the Piston Cup and gain the Dinoco sponsorship!

Mia and Tia

Mia and Tia are identical twin sisters who are McQueen's biggest fans. They eventually move to Radiator Springs and work as waitresses at Flo's café.

Biggest fans

1. One sunny day, Mia and Tia were watching Lightning McQueen after a race. They were his biggest fans. They even used Rust-eze, just like him!

2. "He's a dream car," they sighed. But McQueen was so busy talking to news vans and reporter cars that he didn't even notice them.

3. Then, Mia and Tia heard that Lightning McQueen's new racing headquarters was in Radiator Springs. So, they set off to meet their hero!

4. But Mia and Tia weren't the only ones who had heard that McQueen was in town. "We'll never get through this crowd!" cried Tia, when they arrived.

5. "We've come all this way and we still can't speak to him," sighed Mia. "Let's get a drink instead," suggested Tia. So, they headed to Flo's café.

6. At the café, Flo was rushed off her wheels. She was moving about so fast that she knocked into some oil drums and they began to topple over!

7. Mia and Tia quickly stopped the oil drums from spilling. "You girls are pretty nifty movers!" said Flo. "Would you like to come and work for me?"

8. "Yes, we sure would!" the girls agreed. Pretty soon, they were whizzing around Flo's café. Mia and Tia soon became popular with all the customers!

9. That evening, just as Flo's café was about to close, one customer that Mia and Tia hadn't expected to see, arrived. It was Lightning McQueen!

10. Mia and Tia served him a special oil drink, while they listened to him tell some exciting racing stories. They were so happy to finally meet their hero!

The end

About the story

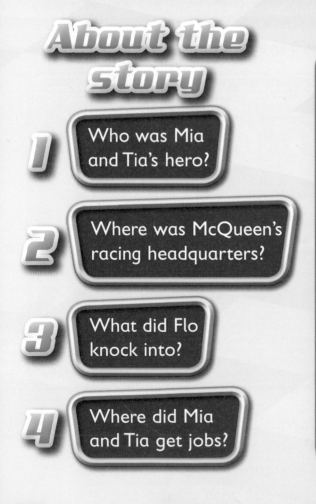

1 Who was Mia and Tia's hero?

2 Where was McQueen's racing headquarters?

3 What did Flo knock into?

4 Where did Mia and Tia get jobs?

Answers: 1. Lightning McQueen. 2. Radiator Springs. 3. Some oil drums. 4. At Flo's café.

4 What can you see in the sky?

5 What object is in the crowd above? Colour in the dotted sections to find out.

6 What colour is The King?

Answers: 1. 3 cars are at the finish line. 2. Sticking his tongue out. 3. Detail c. 4. A helicopter. 5. A trophy 6. Blue.

Who will win?

The King, Lightning McQueen and Chick Hicks are speeding around the racetrack! Can you work out who will win?

The King

Lightning McQueen

Chick Hicks

Out of fuel!

A burst tyre!

Winner!

Answer: Lightning McQueen will win.

Make Mack shine

Give Mack a polish by adding some bright, shiny colours!

17

Speedy snap

Ask a friend to join you for a speedy game of snap!

You will need: 14 pieces of paper, each big enough to cover one of the cars below.

How to play

This is a game for two players. Both players should have a quick look at the cars on each page, before covering them up with pieces of paper. Taking it in turns, pick up one piece of paper on the left page and then pick up the piece of paper on the right page where you think the matching car is. Put both pieces of paper back if you are not correct and remove them both if you are correct. The player who matches up the most cars and finishes with the most pieces of paper, wins!

Pit stop page

Lightning McQueen and Chick Hicks are taking a break from the big race! Answer these questions to help them get back on the track.

1 Which poster has more red cars?

a PISTON CUP

b PISTON CUP

2 Who is having their wheel replaced?

3 Can you match the spanners on the ground with their place in the toolbox?

a

b

c

20

Answers: 1. 2. Chick Hicks. 3. a - 3, b - 1, c - 2. The hose nozzles are a different shape. 5. b.

1 2 3

5

Which oil can doesn't appear in the big picture? Tick the box.

a

b

c

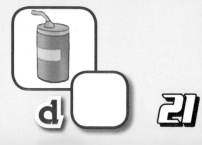

d

Prize puzzle

McQueen is dreaming about all of the prizes he will get for winning the Piston Cup! Can you finish this puzzle and find the piece that doesn't fit?

a   b   c   d   e

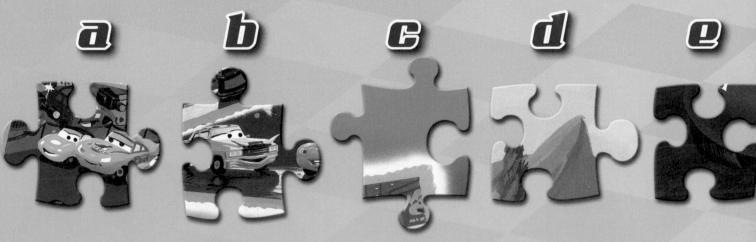

22

Answer: 1 - b, 2 - e, 3 - c, 4 - a. Piece d doesn't fit.

Brighten Boost

Give Boost a burst of colour, using the small picture to guide you.

Boost

Answers: 1. Sally 2. Tyre c.

Find the Ferrari

This Ferrari is a very fast car! Can you find the other Ferrari on the page? Don't mistake him for McQueen!

Answer: f is the other Ferrari.

Racing mural

1. One day, Doc Hudson decided it was time to brighten up the Radiator Springs Racing Museum. "Could you paint a mural on this wall?" he asked Ramone.

2. "No problem! It will be nice to give visitors to the town something new to look at," Ramone agreed. He went to fetch his paints straight away.

3. Ramone spent all day painting an exciting picture on the museum wall. "Looking good!" he thought. The picture was full of action and bright colours.

4. The mural showed two local heroes, Doc and McQueen, in a race. "Great job, Ramone!" cried the crowd, who had gathered to see the finished picture.

5. However, when McQueen saw it, he wasn't pleased. "It looks like I'm going to lose the race," he grumbled. "My fans wouldn't be at all happy about that!"

6. Doc told McQueen that Ramone could change the painting. "It doesn't matter to me who wins the race," he said. "Good!" replied McQueen, crossly.

7. As Ramone changed the mural, McQueen thought about what Doc had said. He realised he'd been selfish. "It doesn't matter who wins," McQueen said.

8. "Don't worry, pal, I have the perfect solution!" Ramone cried, grinning. Everyone waited, excitedly, to see what Ramone would paint!

9. Finally, the mural was revealed. "I think this will give visitors a fair picture of what our town is all about," Ramone cried and everyone laughed.

10. The mural showed McQueen and Doc tied. Ramone had finished it by adding Mater ahead of them, winning the race in his own special way!

The end

About the story

1 Who wanted to brighten up the Racing Museum?

2 What did Ramone paint on the wall?

3 Why wasn't McQueen pleased with the first mural?

4 Who won in the final mural?

Answers: 1. Doc Hudson. 2. A mural. 3. It looked like he was going to lose the race. 4. Mater.

Shield sequence

Doc Hudson is remembering his racing days! Can you help him complete these sequences by correctly colouring the white shield in each row?

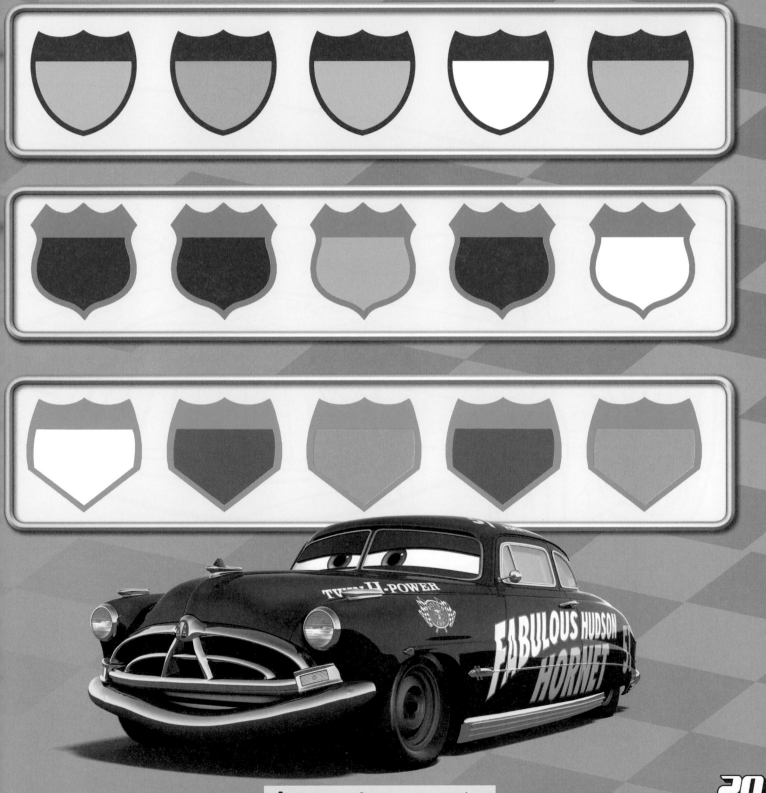

Answer: a - pink, b - red, c - orange.

Chick's colours

Chick has raced right off the track! Give him some colour to cheer him up.

30

Race car changes

Can you spot five differences in picture 2, before McQueen races away? Colour a wheel each time you spot a difference!

Answer: 1. The eyes have moved. 2. The flash is a different colour. 3. The tyre is a different colour. 4. The headlamp is missing. 5. The blue lightning bolt is missing.

Colour the cups

Will Chick Hicks or Lightning McQueen win the Piston Cup? Play this colourful game to find out!

You will need: A dice, a green pen and a red pen.

1

2

3

4

5

6

Chick Hicks

How to play

This is a game for two players. Decide who will be Chick Hicks and who will be Lightning McQueen. Take it in turns to throw the dice and colour in the section of your cup that matches the number thrown. If you have already coloured that section, miss a turn. The first player to colour in all the sections of their cup is the winner.

1

2

3

4

5 6

Lightning McQueen

Odd Hot Rod out

Can you spot the odd Hot Rod out in each row?

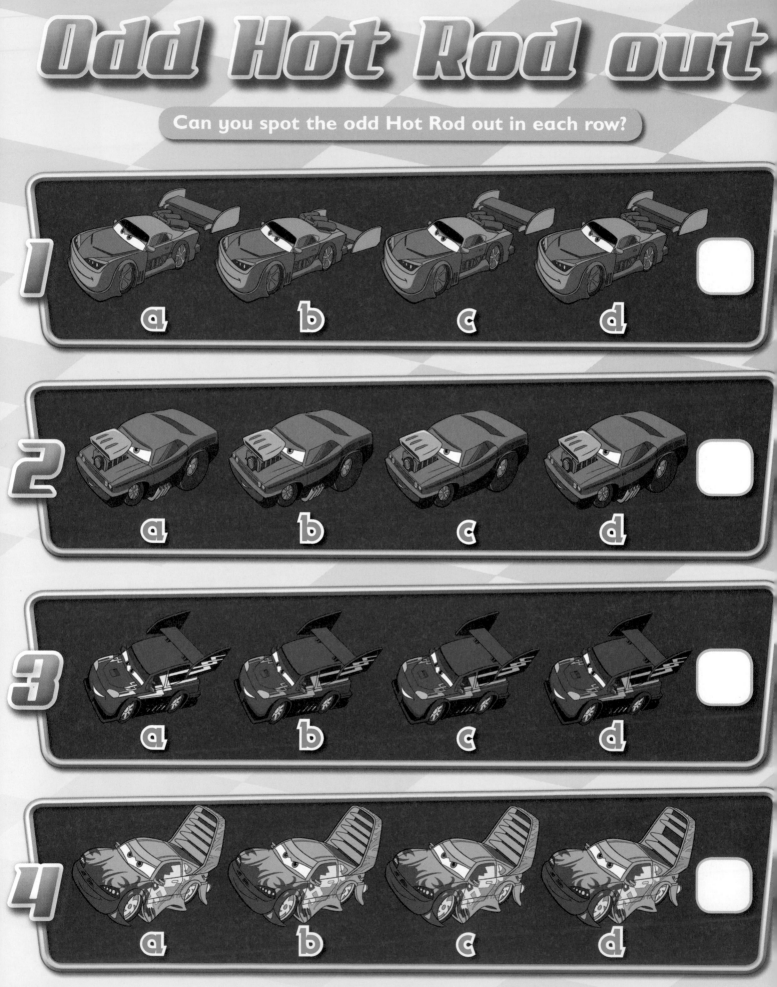

Answers: 1-b, 2-c, 3-a, 4-d.

Tyre teaser

Lightning McQueen is racing again! How many tyre changes will he make before he crosses the finish line?

START

FINISH

Write your answer in the box.

Answer: McQueen will make 9 tyre changes.

35

Dinoco double

Stick this page on to card and then cut out the hanger. Fold it over and glue the backs together. Now it's ready to hang on your door!

You will need: Card, scissors and glue.

Fold here

© Disney/Pixar

© Disney/Pixar

Disney · PIXAR
THE WORLD OF
Cars

ONLY
COOL
CARS
ALLOWED!

Disney · PIXAR
THE WORLD OF
Cars

95 Lightning McQueen

The KING says KEEP OUT!

Fold here

Big crash changes

McQueen has escaped a big crash on the racetrack! Can you spot five differences in picture 2?

Colour a flag each time you spot a difference!

Answer:
1. McQueen's eyes have moved. 2. The orange car has changed colour. 3. The number on the purple car is different. 4. There is another tyre in the air. 5. The number on Chick's headlight is missing.

On the road

McQueen is on his way to another big race.
Answer these questions before he arrives!

1 Who sponsors McQueen?

2 Which model of McQueen isn't part of a matching pair?

38

3 What colour is McQueen? Colour in the poster of him!

4 How many Piston Cups can you spot in the scene?

5 Which of these tools is not on the wall?

a b c d e

Answers: 1. Rust-eze. 2. Model d is not part of a pair. 3. Red. 4. There are 4 Piston Cups in the scene. 5. Tool c is not on the wall.

Poster pairs

Instead of Rust-eze, McQueen dreams of being sponsored by Dinoco like his hero, The King! Put these promotional posters into pairs. Which poster is not part of a pair?

Answer: The Rust-eze poster is not part of a pair.

Tex message

Which company does Tex own? Starting with the biggest balloon, copy the letters in order of balloon size into the boxes below.

Answer: Tex owns Dinoco.

Hot colours

Give Snot Rod some hot colours, using the small picture to guide you.

Snot Rod

How to play

Decide which pittie each player will be. Place all the counters on the Start/Finish tyre and take it in turns to roll the dice and move around the tyre track. If you land on a big tyre, have an extra turn but if you land on a tyre that has burst, miss a turn. The first player to reach the Start/Finish tyre again is the winner!

1. One sunny day, the residents of Radiator Springs were decorating Main Street, ready for a parade. It was to celebrate the Piston Cup race cars!

2. "Hoo-eee!" Mater chuckled, as he drove around and looked at all the bright colours. "I wonder if I can get a part in the parade?" he thought.

3. Mater decided to ask his friend, Doc Hudson, if he could join in the parade. "I'm sorry, Mater. You've never raced in the Piston Cup," Doc told him.

4. Then, Mater found McQueen being hosed down by Red for his starring role in the parade. "Sorry, the parade is for race cars, not tow trucks," McQueen said.

5. Mater wasn't very happy. "Why do they only have parades for race cars?" he grumbled. Mater joined the crowd and waited for the parade to start.

6. Suddenly, a loud popping noise came from the end of Main Street. Mack, who was pulling McQueen's float, had overheated. "I've got to pull over!" he cried.

7. McQueen raced over to Mater straight away. "Mater, I need your help!" he said. "You need me to be on your float?" Mater replied, excitedly.

8. "Well, not exactly. But we could really use a tow truck!" McQueen explained. "No problem, buddy!" Mater said happily, as he backed up.

9. "Look at me!" Mater laughed, as he towed the floats in front of the cheering crowd. He was happy to help and excited to be part of the parade.

10. But Mater wasn't just part of the parade. He was right at the front, leading the race cars. "You're a star!" McQueen told a very happy Mater.

The end

About the story

1 What was the parade to celebrate?

2 Why wasn't Mater allowed in the parade?

3 Who was hosing down McQueen?

4 What was Mater's part in the parade?

Answers: 1. The Piston Cup race cars. 2. It was only for race cars. 3. Red. 4. He was at the front, towing the floats!

Fans' flags

Join these racing fans and answer these quick questions!

1 Which cars are on the big screens? Colour them in!

How many of each colour flag can you find in the picture? Write your answers in the boxes.

Answers: 1. Lightning McQueen and The King. 2. Red - 6, blue - 5, green - 4.

49

Piston Cup pile-up

There's a pile-up on the race track. Quickly answer these questions before anyone else crashes!

1 How many cars have crashed?

2 What colour is car 76?

3 Which number below does not appear on a car in the big picture? Tick the box when you've worked it out!

21   16   51   30   95

4 Who is sticking out his tongue?

5 What speedy word is following behind Lightning McQueen?

6 Can you spot a flying tyre?

Answers: 1. 5 cars have crashed. 2. Purple. 3. 30. 4. Lightning McQueen. 5. Zoom. 6. In the dust cloud behind the crash.

The circuit

Join McQueen, The King and Chick Hicks for some fast fun as they race around this circuit!

You will need: A dice, two counters and a pen.

Player card 1

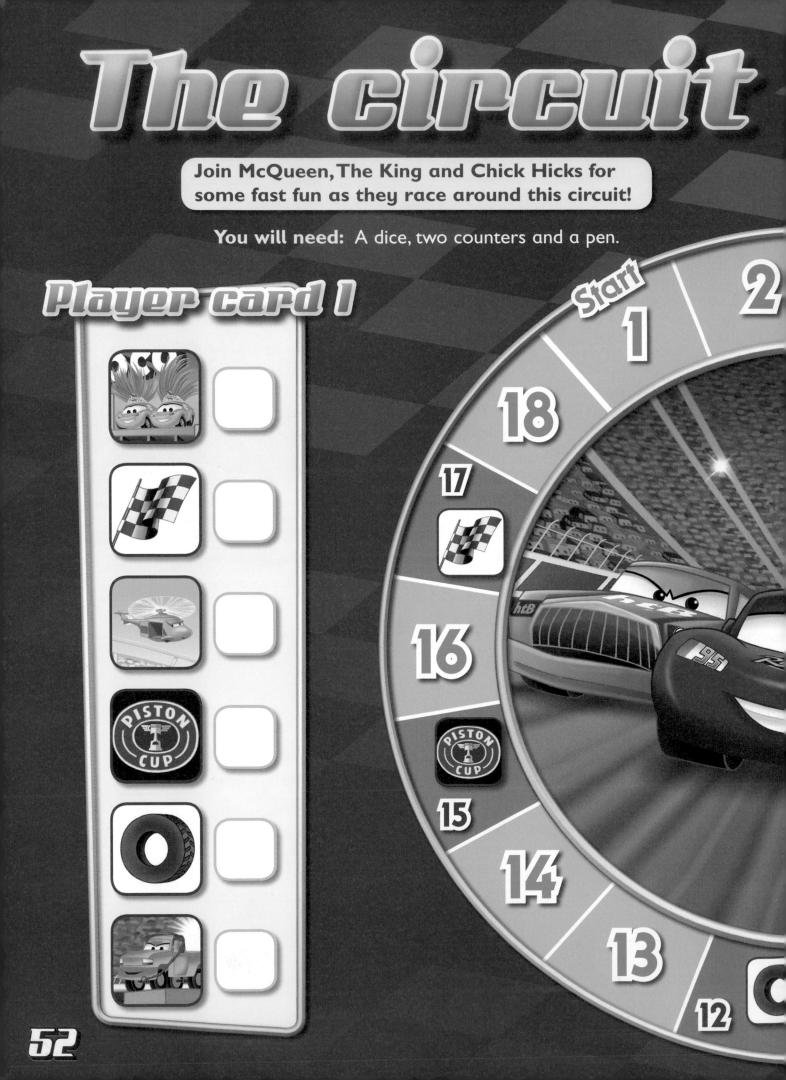

How to play

This is a game for two players. Choose a player card each, then take it in turns to roll the dice and move your counter around the board. If you land on a racing object, tick the matching box on your player card. The first player to tick all of their boxes is a race winner, just like these cool cars!

3

4

5

6

7

8

9

10

11

Player card 2

Winning name

Lightning McQueen is dreaming of winning the Piston Cup. Which row of flags has the correct spelling of his name? Tick the box.

1. Lightiing

2. Lyyyntning

3. Lightning

4. Ligthnnig

Answer: Row 3.

Cool colours

Give DJ a dash of colour, using the small picture to guide you.

DJ

Speedy snapper

Make this great game to play with all your friends! Just cut out the square on the opposite page and follow the instructions below.

1
Place the square face down and fold along the solid white lines so that the four corners meet in the centre.

2
Turn the square over and fold along the red lines so that the four corners meet in the centre.

3
Fold it in half, with the colours on the inside, and crease to make a rectangle. Now, fold again to make a square.

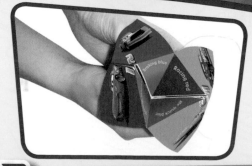

1
To hold the game, push your thumbs and forefingers under the pictures.

2
Ask a friend to choose a number and then open and close the game that number of times.

3
Finally, ask them to choose a colour from the inside and lift up the corner to see what they have to do!

Go faster green

Race around the room

Pit stop pink

Start your engine

1

2

Oil change orange

Cruise like a car

Braking blue

Fuel up with food

Be quick blue

Rev up for a race

Take a test drive

Racing red

3

4

Parking purple

Warm up your wheels

Start to steer

You win yellow

57

To the finish

McQueen is determined to win this race! Help him along the track to the finish line, making five pit stops on the way.

Start

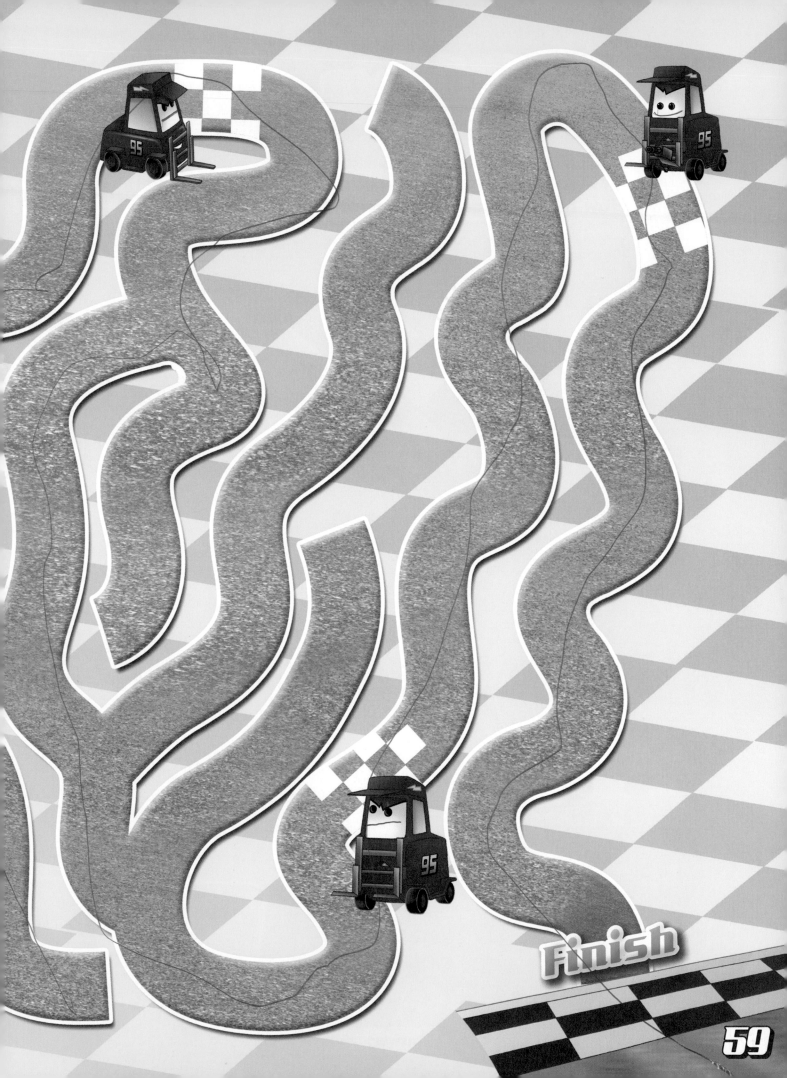

Finish

Find the flags

McQueen is dreaming about crossing the finish line!
How many chequered flags can you find on the page?

95

I can find [ ] flags.

60

Answer: 9 flags.

Racing colours

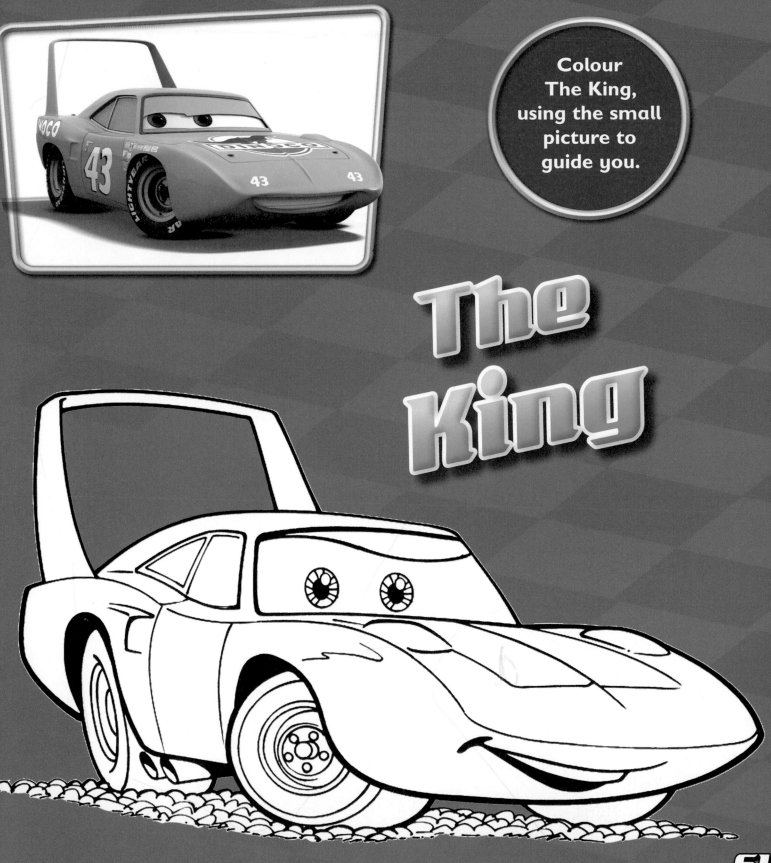

Colour
The King,
using the small
picture to
guide you.

The King

Lightning's lead

Can you finish these questions before the winner crosses the line?

1 How many lightning bolts can you spot? *6*

2 What number is on McQueen's headlight? *95*

Chick Hicks

Lightning McQueen

3 Which detail below isn't from the picture? *d*

a b c d e

62

4 Who does not have a pit crew chief?

The King

5 What word is written on the race track below?

6 What lap are the cars on?

speed

Answers: 1. lightning bolts. 2. 95. 3. d. 4. Lightning McQueen. 5. speed. 6. Lap 245.

Jump start

Jump start your car and collect as many points as possible!

You will need: A different colour counter for each player.

line up here

2 points

How to play

Line up your counters and then take it in turns to flick them forward, lining up again after each round. Keep a record of the points from where your counter lands. The counter with the most points in total after three rounds wins the Piston Cup! Write the winner's name in the winner box at the bottom.

4 points

6 points

Winner!

The pit crew

Which pit crew changed McQueen's flat tyre? Do the sums to find the pit crew with the answer that matches the number on his tyre.

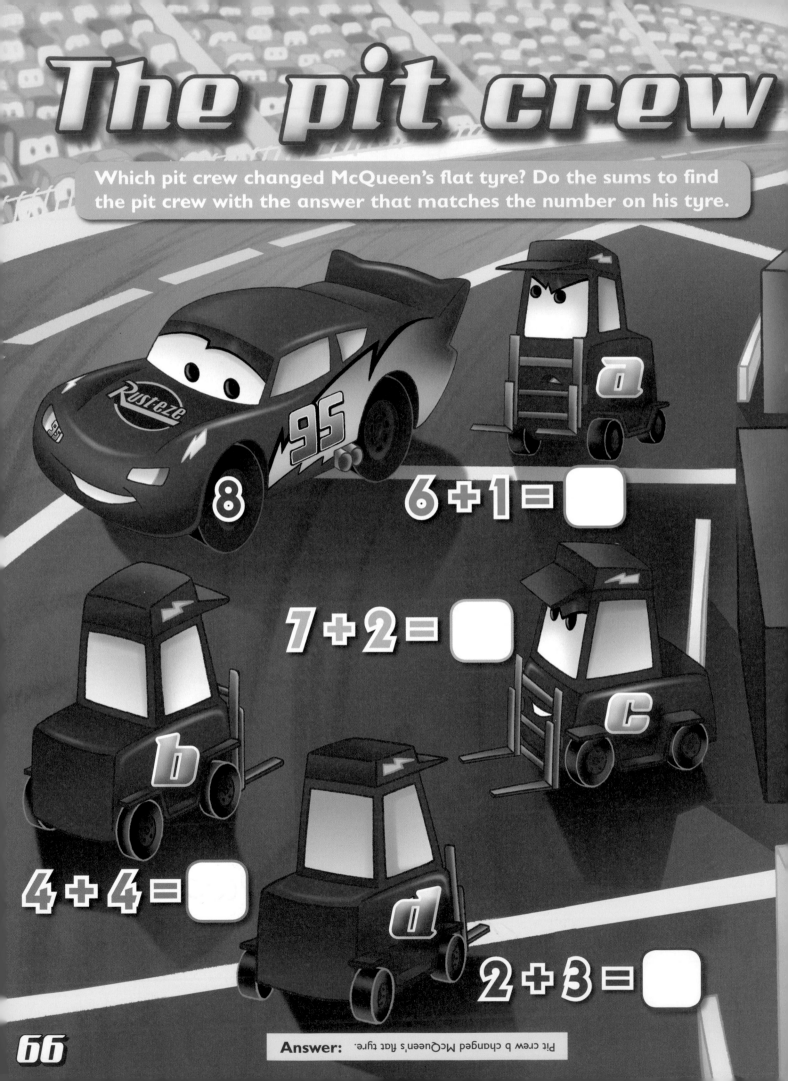

8

6+1=☐

7+2=☐

4+4=☐

2+3=☐

Answer: Pit crew b changed McQueen's flat tyre.

Flying colours

Give Wingo some winning colours, using the small picture to guide you.

Wingo

The finish line

Can you answer these questions and cross the finish line?

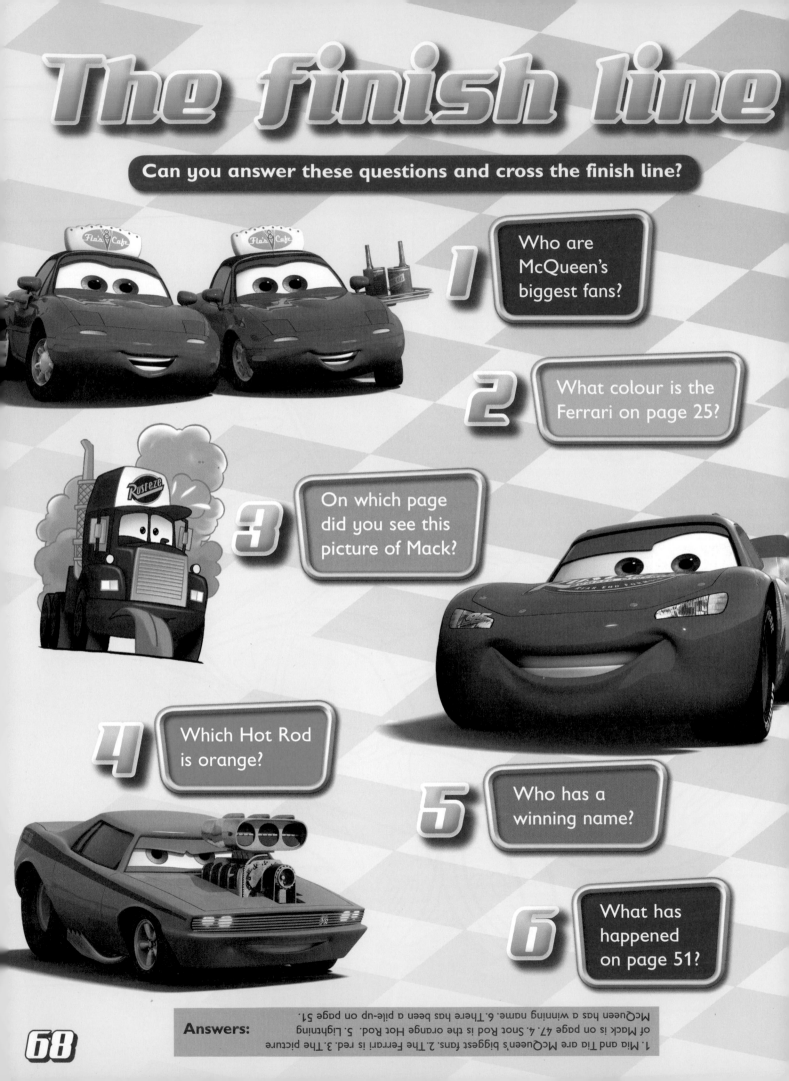

1 Who are McQueen's biggest fans?

2 What colour is the Ferrari on page 25?

3 On which page did you see this picture of Mack?

4 Which Hot Rod is orange?

5 Who has a winning name?

6 What has happened on page 51?

Answers: 1. Mia and Tia are McQueen's biggest fans. 2. The Ferrari is red. 3. The picture of Mack is on page 47. 4. Snot Rod is the orange Hot Rod. 5. Lightning McQueen has a winning name. 6. There has been a pile-up on page 51.

ADVERTISEMENT